Audubon's Ducks

A Book of Days

GALISON BOOKS
GMG PUBLISHING, NEW YORK

A GALISON BOOK
Published by GMG Publishing Corp.
25 West 43rd Street
New York, NY 10036

ISBN 0-939456-46-X

Designer: Diana Howard
Managing Editor: Catherine Grandsard
Publisher: Gerald Galison

All illustrations by John James Audubon
from *The Birds of America*.
Courtesy of the National Gallery of Art, Washington
Gift of Mrs. Walter B. James

Cover illustration:
American Scoter Duck

Printed in Japan

*A*merica's greatest ornithological painter, John James Audubon (1785–1851), did not begin publication of *The Birds of America*, his first work and the source of the illustrations for this *Book of Days*, until he was 42 years old. Various unsuccessful business ventures in New York and frontier Kentucky (Audubon neglected his affairs to pursue his enthusiasm for nature and drawing) precipitated his desperate decision to become a professional artist.

About a year after declaring bankruptcy in 1819, Audubon conceived the idea of publishing lavish illustrations and descriptions of all the bird species in North America. By 1824, he had amassed enough drawings to present to a publisher, but received no encouragement in his own country. Happily for Audubon, interest both in ornithology and America was keen among the British upper classes, and his efforts in England met with considerable success. Late in 1826, Edinburgh engraver William Lizars agreed to undertake the enormous job of publishing Audubon's work. However, while Audubon was in London soliciting subscribers to finance the project, Lizars abandoned *Birds* after engraving only 10 plates. Audubon finally was able to continue the printing with Robert Havell, a respected London engraver and publisher.

The waterfowl illustrations reprinted in *Book of Days* are only a small number of the 435 color plates Audubon published by 1838. Each bird is depicted in its natural setting, interacting with other birds or with prey or predators, and is drawn to life size. (However, even the book's oversize format—29½ by 39½ inches—was not big enough to accommodate the largest birds comfortably; some were fitted in by drooping their long necks toward their feet.) Unlike previous authors of ornithological books, Audubon actually went into the fields, woods, and swamps (often for months at a time) to study live birds. He then shot and drew them immediately, before their colors or his impressions of them could fade. The results of Audubon's painstaking work will live on forever.

Ruddy Duck

FULIGULA RUBIDA

female adult young male, second spring

January

1	12	23
2	13	24
3	14	25
4	15	26
5	16	27
6	17	28
7	18	29
8	19	30
9	20	31
10	21	
11	22	

Golden-eye Duck

CLANGULA VULGARIS

male, summer plumage

February

1 ....

2 ....

3 ....

4 ....

5 ....

6 ....

7 ....

8 ....

9 ....

10 ....

11 ....

12 ....

13 ....

14 ....

15 ....

16 ....

17 ....

18 ....

19 ....

20 ....

21 ....

22 ....

23 ....

24 ....

25 ....

26 ....

27 ....

28 ....

29 ....

Pied Duck

FULIGULA LABRADORA

1 male adult 2 female

March

1

2

3

4

5

6

7

8

9

10

11

12

13

14

15

16

17

18

19

20

21

22

23

24

25

26

27

28

29

30

31

Red-headed Duck

FULIGULA FERINA

1 male 2 female

April

1

2

3

4

5

6

7

8

9

10

11

12

13

14

15

16

17

18

19

20

21

22

23

24

25

26

27

28

29

30

Scaup Duck

FULIGULA MARILA

1 male 2 female

May

1

2

3

4

5

6

7

8

9

10

11

12

13

14

15

16

17

18

19

20

21

22

23

24

25

26

27

28

29

30

31

Long-tailed Duck

FULIGULA GLACIALIS

1 male, summer plumage 2 male, winter 3 female, young

June

1

2

3

4

5

6

7

8

9

10

11

12

13

14

15

16

17

18

19

20

21

22

23

24

25

26

27

28

29

30

Red-breasted Merganser

MERGUS SERRATOR

1 male 2 female

July

1

2

3

4

5

6

7

8

9

10

11

12

13

14

15

16

17

18

19

20

21

22

23

24

25

26

27

28

29

30

31

Shoveller Duck

ANAS CLYPEATA

1 male 2 female

August

1	12	23
2	13	24
3	14	25
4	15	26
5	16	27
6	17	28
7	18	29
8	19	30
9	20	31
10	21	
11	22	

Gadwall Duck

ANAS STREPERA

1 male 2 female

September

1

2

3

4

5

6

7

8

9

10

11

12

13

14

15

16

17

18

19

20

21

22

23

24

25

26

27

28

29

30

Blue-winged Teal

ANAS DISCORS

1 male 2 female

October

1

2

3

4

5

6

7

8

9

10

11

12

13

14

15

16

17

18

19

20

21

22

23

24

25

26

27

28

29

30

31

American Scoter Duck

FULIGULA AMERICANA

1 male   2 female

November

1

2

3

4

5

6

7

8

9

10

11

12

13

14

15

16

17

18

19

20

21

22

23

24

25

26

27

28

29

30

Bemaculated Duck

ANAS GLOCITANS

young male in December

December

1

2

3

4

5

6

7

8

9

10

11

12

13

14

15

16

17

18

19

20

21

22

23

24

25

26

27

28

29

30

31

Notes

Notes

Notes

Notes

Notes